PENGUIN BOOKS

NEVER GIVE UP

Jacky Fleming went to a suffragette school in London. She emerged awesomely uneducated due to the teachers' inexplicable preference for Latin as a first language. A year at Chelsea School of Art and a degree in Fine Art at Leeds University greatly improved her table-football technique. Other qualifications include A– for posture and a silver medal in Latin-American dancing. A brief stint in the art department of a London periodical was followed by eleven years' teaching art as a foreign language. Jacky lives in Yorkshire and still hates cooking.

Her cartoons have been published by the BBC, The Women's Press, Virago, Leeds Postcards, Aberdeen University Press, Longman, *Spare Rib*, The Open University and others. Penguin also publishes her popular first book of cartoons, *Be a Bloody Train Driver*.

JACKY FLEMING

never give up

PENGUIN BOOKS

PENGUIN BOOKS

Published by the Penguin Group
Penguin Books Ltd, 27 Wrights Lane, London W8 5TZ, England
Penguin Books USA Inc., 375 Hudson Street, New York, New York 10014, USA
Penguin Books Australia Ltd, Ringwood, Victoria, Australia
Penguin Books Canada Ltd, 10 Alcorn Avenue, Toronto, Ontario, Canada M4V 3B2
Penguin Books (NZ) Ltd, 182–190 Wairau Road, Auckland 10, New Zealand

Penguin Books Ltd, Registered Offices: Harmondsworth, Middlesex, England

First published in book form 1992
1 3 5 7 9 10 8 6 4 2

Printed in England by Clays Ltd, St Ives plc

don't hold your breath
JF

I'd never marry you
another narrow escape
JF

you're going to be OLD
SINGLE and LONELY

and only YOU could make
it sound SO ATTRACTIVE
JF

apparently if a woman still hasn't married by thirty-five there's only a 5% chance she ever will

JF

Dear Katie,
I grew up thinking that one day Prince Charming would come and sweep me off my feet. Each time I think it's finally happened then it wears off.

Now I'm beginning to think I've been conned by romantic twaddle.

Have I?

Dear Rosie,

Of course not. Lower your standards and keep trying.

Fanny is a waitress. Because she has to WORK for a living she doesn't look as good as she could

AUDIENCE WONDER IF THEY LOOK AS MISERABLE AS SHE DOES

Everyone in the cafe is very nice considering they are single, lonely and depressed. They even make a birthday cake for one of their regulars which just makes everyone feel worse.

INCLUDING THE AUDIENCE

Fanny lives with a gay man. Does this mean she's AVOIDING something? Is there something about heterosexual men she can't HANDLE?

It certainly looks that way

Meanwhile back at the cafe one of the older waitresses is rushed to hospital and dies. This is a direct result of being single.

PANIC RIPPLES THROUGH THE AUDIENCE

Illness and death can only be avoided one way...

Meet Johnny, just out of jail and lonely as HELL. He wants Fanny but she doesn't want him. Which is odd because he's fairly handsome and she IS single.

Clearly the woman is a bit nicked

Luckily for Fanny, Johnny won't take no for an answer and pesters her relentlessly.

Johnny recognizes this as DEFENSIVE behaviour and nothing personal.

Finally we discover why Fanny's been acting so STRANGELY. Her last partner used to beat her up.

Fanny's neurotic defenses crumble and they can finally look forward to a lifetime of domestic bliss

They curl up together and sleep like spoons

THIS IS NOT ONE OF THOSE NASTY FILMS ABOUT SEX AND THE SINGLE WOMAN

Not forgetting the OTHERS who are still out there, single and lonely.

AUDIENCE LEAVES CHASTENED, FULLY PREPARED TO MARRY ANYONE WITH A PULSE

…and they lived happily ever after
until the birth of their first child when
he went to pieces and she went off sex entirely.'

women have finally realised there is
only one source of true happiness

chocolate mousse

JF

Little boys see mummy as HUGE and all powerful

this image never entirely fades

In order to become men they must BREAK AWAY from mummy

this pattern also never changes

As it was never his job to look after mummy, he never does

this makes women 'demanding'

But it **IS** mummy's job to look after him

this means men don't need to be demanding

Girls, on the other hand, never need to break away from mummy because

they will never have to look after themselves...

just everyone else.

It's best to learn this early on JF

Dear Katie,

Since the birth of my baby I've been terribly depressed. I feel trapped and isolated at home, and I miss the stimulus of my job, and going out.

The biggest shock has been that I have no maternal instincts and feel the responsibility for my baby's well-being and safety as a terrifying burden.

What makes it even worse is that I'm perpetually exhausted from lack of sleep.

Dear Mary,

Buck up.

where's daddy?

he's at a workshop for
men who missed their
daddies when they were little

Men are oppressed just as much as women. In fact MORE. WE don't have the right to PATERNITY leave
let me guess - you've been too shy to mention it all these years
JF

Is it only nine months?
I could swear it's been
several years
JF

I can tell you NOW – you're an only child
JF

It only hurts when I MOVE
JF

sex?
how do you
spell that
JF

can I have
a biscuit
can I have a biscuit
can I have a biscuit
can I have
NO

can I have a biscuit
can I have a biscuit
can I have a biscuit
can I have a biscuit

JF

that's not sweeties

I only eat sweeties

JF

it's NOT post natal depression

hey ho

it's not that I don't LIKE children ....

yes it is
JF

No food
Couldn't be
bothered
JF

JF

Selective Hearing Syndrome – female

you are the most desirable, gorgeous, intelligent,
humourous, sexy, compassionate, tender, witty, and
musical woman I have EVER met. I prefer your
company to anyone else's even if you are a bit
moody sometimes

what do you mean by
a bit moody sometimes?

JF

Selective Hearing Syndrome – male

you take NO responsibility for the children,
you NEVER cook, ironing's too 'complicated' for you,
if I asked you what colour the hoover is you wouldn't
know, and you haven't made a bed in fifteen years

bed? now?

JF

PMT SURVIVAL KIT IV

self adhesive
diary stickers

and some useful badges

THIS MAY LOOK
LIKE MY USUAL
UNREASONABLENESS
IT ISN'T.
PMT

DO YOURSELF
A FAVOUR
and
GIVE ME A
WIDE BERTH
PMT PMT

ON
NO ACCOUNT
ALLOW ME TO
DISCUSS
SEPARATION
THIS WEEK
We can discuss it
next week

AVOID ANY
UNNECESSARY
CONVERSATION
ONLY ASK QUESTIONS
WHICH REQUIRE
YES/NO ANSWERS
LEAVE AGAIN PROMPTLY

PMT SURVIVAL KIT V

Home alone

Living alone is so peaceful you could hear a pin drop

Living alone means you can
have the whole bed to yourself

and feel in complete control of your life

It isn't always easy...

but you can get a taste for it

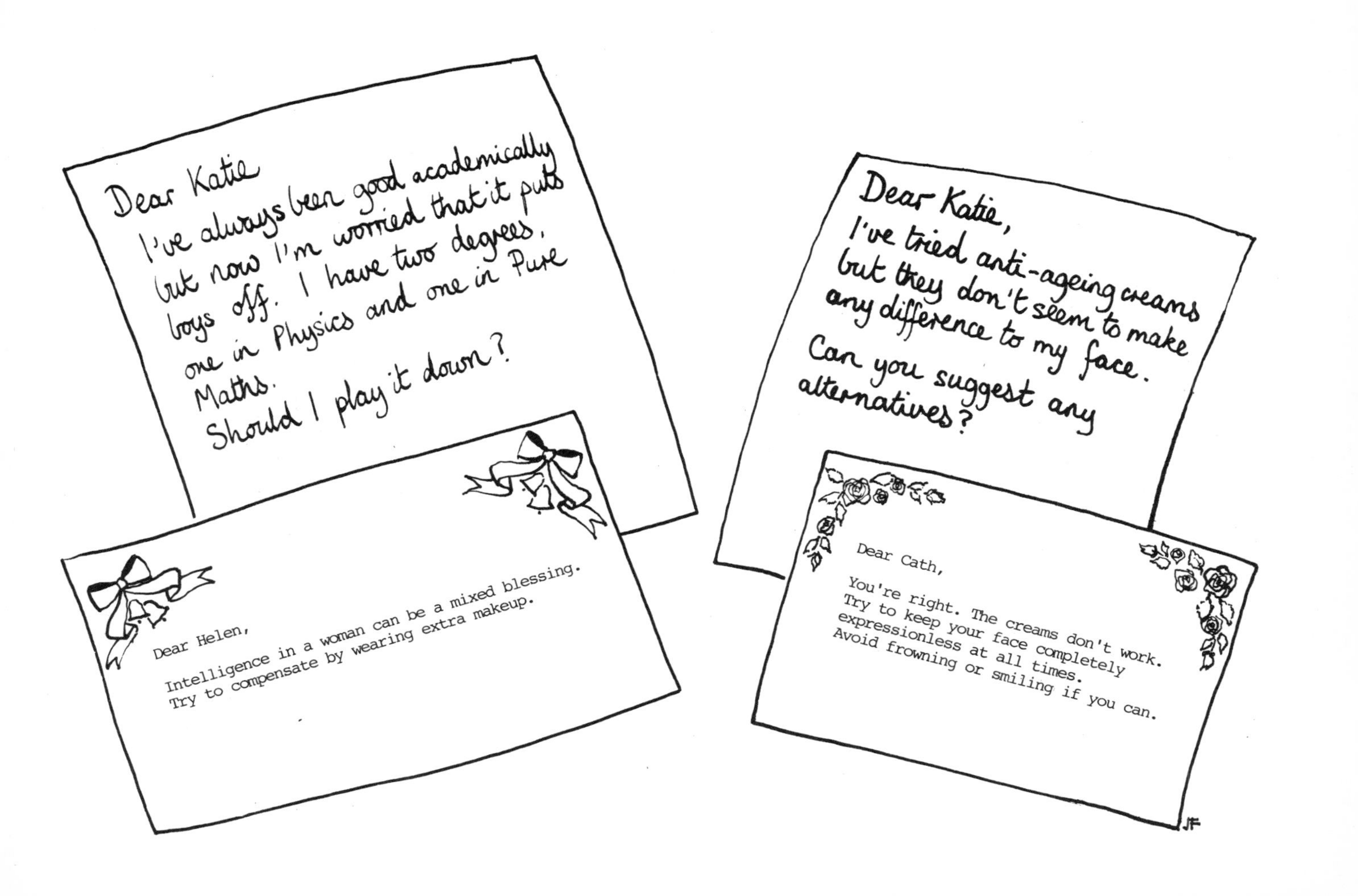
Dear Katie
I've always been good academically but now I'm worried that it puts boys off. I have two degrees, one in Physics and one in Pure Maths.
Should I play it down?
Dear Helen,
Intelligence in a woman can be a mixed blessing.
Try to compensate by wearing extra makeup.
Dear Katie,
I've tried anti-ageing creams but they don't seem to make any difference to my face.
Can you suggest any alternatives?
Dear Cath,
You're right. The creams don't work.
Try to keep your face completely expressionless at all times.
Avoid frowning or smiling if you can.
JF

you don't look like a feminist

WATCH OUT -
we DISGUISE ourselves as human beings until DUSK
JF

TOP GIRL
MAGAZINE
FOR THE LIBERATED WOMAN
COSMETIC SURGERY
The shortcut to shaping up
REAL LIFE TRAUMAS
do they help you lose weight?
THE BATTLE OF THE SEXES
Are you driving your man wild
or driving him away
CORSETS ARE BACK
but this time on our terms
THE POST FEMINIST WOMAN
is not afraid of pornography
YOUR TURN TO PROPOSE
top girls don't wait to be asked
ALL IN THIS MONTH'S
EROTIC EXTRAVAGANZA
JF

and when we're feeling REALLY liberated we even punch ourselves in the face!

Close up

Stand in front of the mirror
and take a GOOD look.
What do you see?

Let's take a closer look.
Have you been neglecting
your knees and elbows?

Is your bottom crying out for an exfoliating scrub?

Have your breasts begun their slow descent?

Take a closer look at your feet.
When did you last PAMPER them?

And when did you last take a
SERIOUS look at your back?

Is your stomach trim and flat, or has the winter bulge got the better of you?

Here are fifty tips to get you looking good

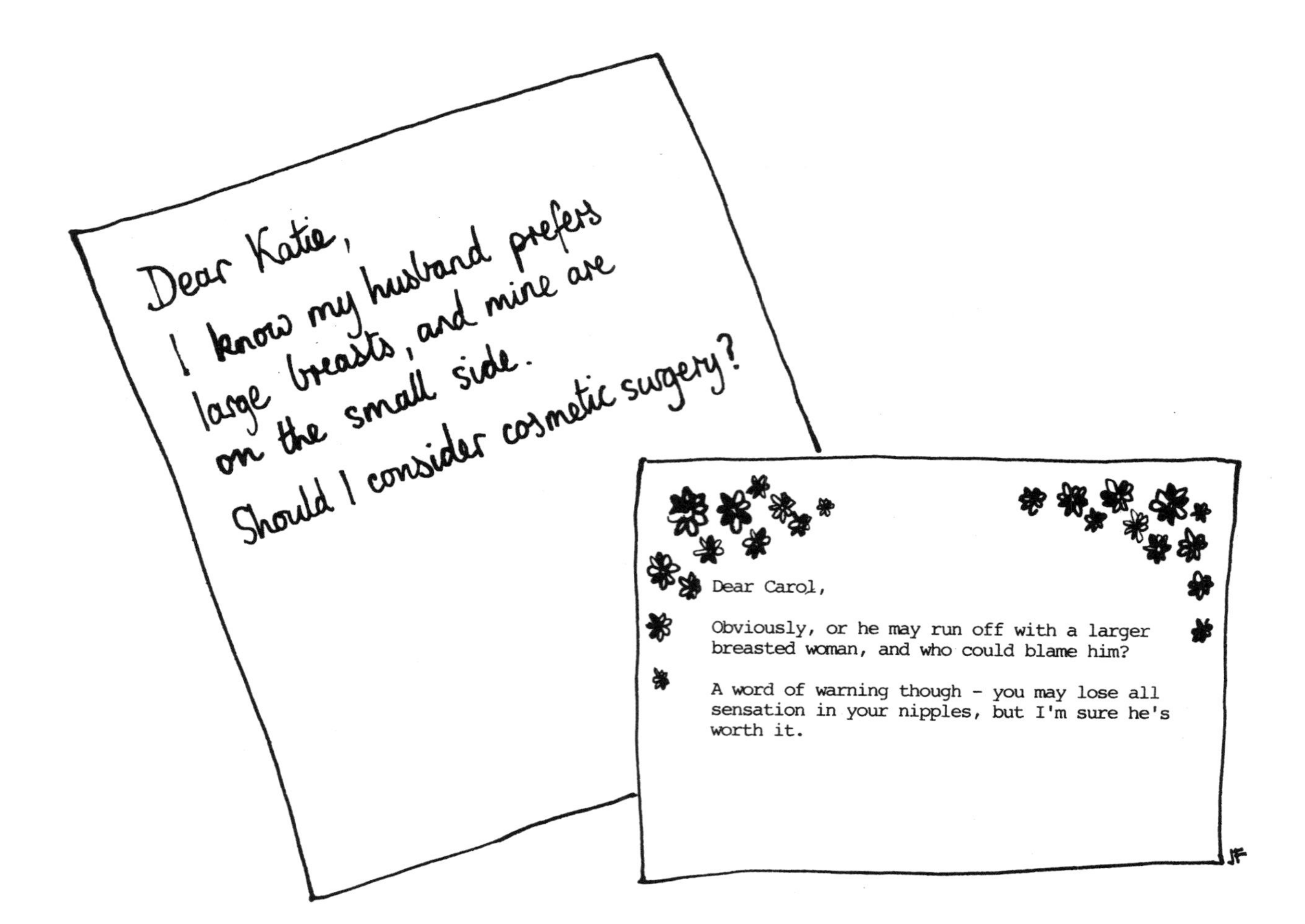
Dear Katie,
I know my husband prefers large breasts, and mine are on the small side.
Should I consider cosmetic surgery?
Dear Carol,
Obviously, or he may run off with a larger breasted woman, and who could blame him?
A word of warning though - you may lose all sensation in your nipples, but I'm sure he's worth it.
JF

JASON QUICK
IT'S STRAYED AGAIN
JF

I found this fabulous little man who just moved my buttocks round to the front. So simple.
JF

Oh do you like it?
I had some of the
bulkier secondary
organs removed
JF

I got this new slim-line brain
and the boys really love it

JF

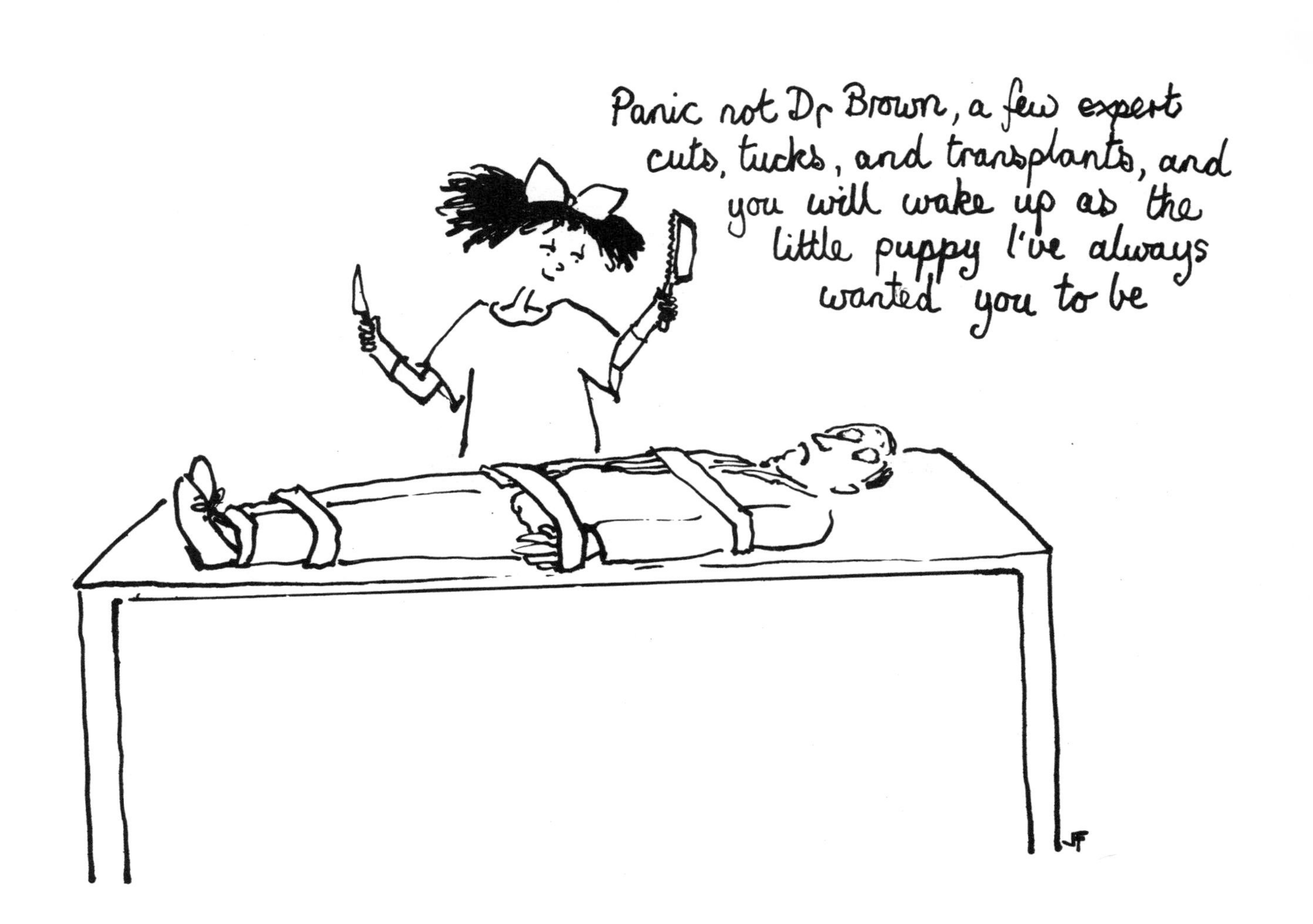
Panic not Dr Brown, a few expert cuts, tucks, and transplants, and you will wake up as the little puppy I've always wanted you to be
JF

if I were thinner

I'd be thinner

JF

you're FAT

said the dinghy to the galleon

Donald you look a prat

then he unbuttoned my blouse...

and what did he say?

oh no not DAMART

JF

LOOK everyone she's got LEGS

These are not MY legs I merely borrowed them for the occasion

JF

if you're feeling
gift wrapped
LOOK OUT

I say Kath
THAT'S jolly sexy
JF

I'll ring you back.
Jane's having one of her
'I will if I want to'
frenzies
JF

REAL chic is
always ahead of
its time

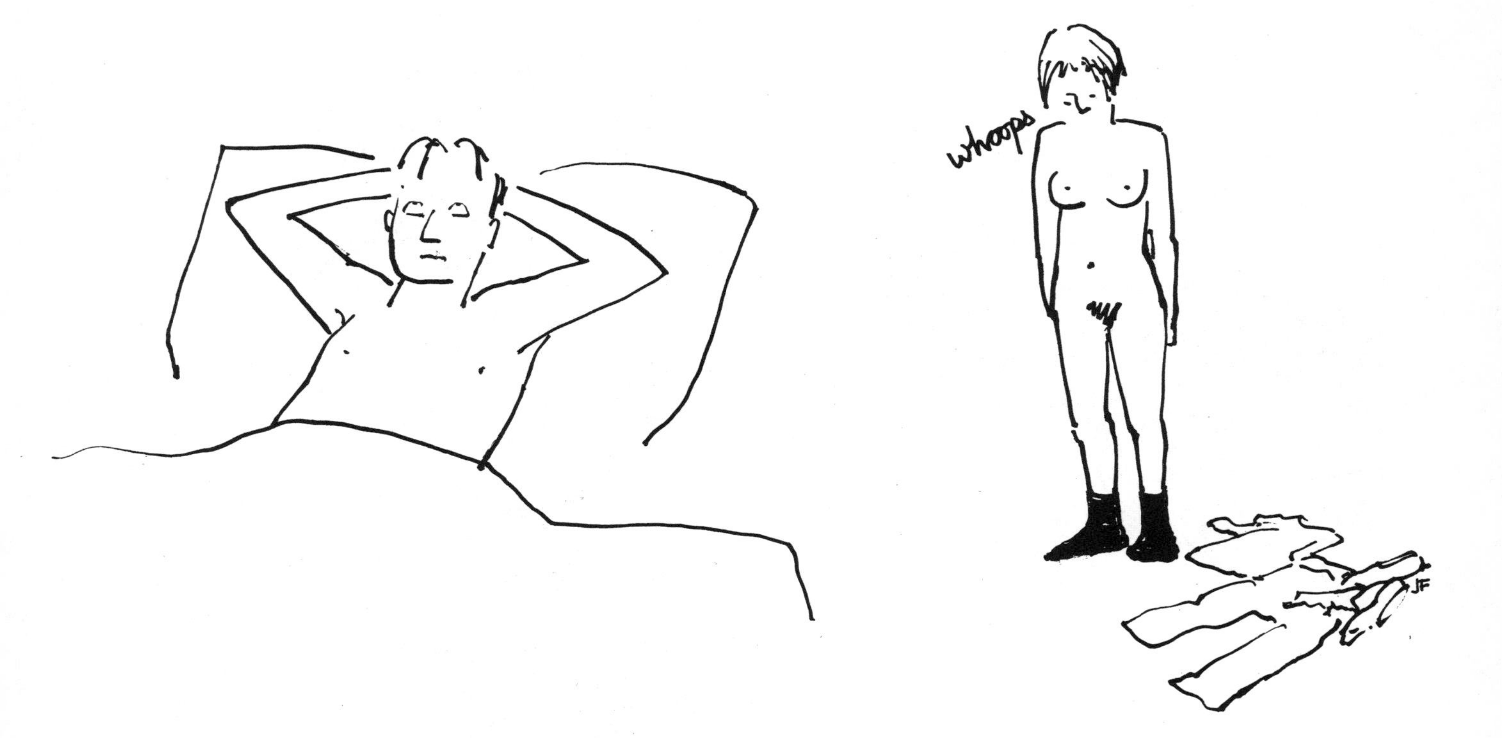
whoops
JF

tomorrow I'll wear
something TERRIFIC

I'll wear what I like

Dear Katie,

I have a wonderful career which I enjoy immensely. Due to recent promotion I earn a higher salary than my husband. We have a good marriage, but he is reacting badly to the difference in our wages.

Dear Sally,

Feminist notions have wrecked many a good marriage. Go part-time and I'll wager he perks up.

JF

women have spread themselves
too thin with this juggling of
marriage, career, and children

right as usual dear,
marriage will have to go

'Droves of burnt out, infertile, unfulfilled women are leaving their careers and returning home, cheated of love and children by the hollow promises of feminism'

HOW could we have been so FOOLISH?
All those YEARS when we could
have been breeding
and cooking
and now we're just
hollow wombs
JF

Teaching is its own reward

and what's really fascinating about the Renaissance is..
JF

It may shock you to know that I was young once
JF

Do you take drugs Miss?

funny you should ask Robert
I thought I might drop a
few hundred valium
later tonight

JF

I HATE art
oh good
JF

I have never BRIBED a child before, Michael

you can all fuck off home now
JF

no I wouldn't rather be a housewife
I'd rather have good pay good job opportunities
childcare facilities justice decent contraception
abortion on demand safe streets comfortable
clothes less of your lip and a bit of RESPECT.

And a whisky.

JF

Dear Katie,
Sometimes my husband gets drunk and becomes aggressive. Last week he kicked the cat. Most of the time he's an easy going sort of man.

Am I doing something to upset him?

Dear Janice,

Probably. Perhaps you've been wearing a colour he doesn't like. Try to find out what he does like and keep to it.
Some men are very sensitive.

JF

If he was so VIOLENT towards her
I fail to comprehend why she didn't
merely LEAVE him. I myself have
a little pied à terre in St James's
which I frequent when occasion
demands
VF

the suggestion that we're out of touch is preposterous. I have even travelled on the underground, I think
JF

He seems a thoroughly decent fellow
to me, who has obligingly provided
regular beatings to a remarkably
ungrateful wife

There are of course many reasons why
DEFINING rape is not a simple process –
had she perhaps been pleasant towards him,
was she attractively clothed, had she
consented on PREVIOUS occasions,
had she been breastfeeding in his presence...

...did she say NO in such a way that it could be understood as YES, did she fight him off in a manner which could have implied consent?

All these things make it very DIFFICULT for a man to understand the messages he's being given

JF

yes means YES
and no means

NO

I expect you'll want that repeating

fancy a night out?

no, I don't

All things bright and beautiful
except for all women
All creatures great and small
except for all women
All things wise and wonderful
except for all women
The Lord God made them all
although how He could make such a blunder
I will never be able to fathom unless it was
to do the cleaning

JF

SOCIETY FOR THE
PROTECTION
OF THE UNBORN CHILD

Society for the protection of
children who've already been
born from prejudiced old
hypocrites like that one over there
JF

Please give generously to support the offspring of innocent priests led astray by wicked women
THANK YOU
JF

IMMACULATE
CONTRACEPTION
you ninny
JF

men have been oppressed
by feminism for too long
We no longer dare to
speak our minds for
fear of being called
SEXIST

JF

why CAN women make sexist jokes and men can't?

who said we were joking?

JF

post feminism
JF